Exploring REDWOOD National Park

by Barbara A. Donovan
illustrated by Ashley Mims

Copyright © by Harcourt, Inc.

Requests for permission to make copies of any part of the work should be addressed to School Permissions and Copyrights, Harcourt, Inc., 6277 Sea Harbor Drive, Orlando, Florida 32887–6777. Fax: 407-345-2418.

HARCOURT and the Harcourt Logo are trademarks of Harcourt, Inc., registered in the United States of America and/or other jurisdictions.

Printed in Mexico

ISBN 10: 0-15-350567-2
ISBN 13: 978-0-15-350567-6

Ordering Options
ISBN 10: 0-15-350335-1 (Grade 5 Below-Level Collection)
ISBN 13: 978-0-15-350335-1 (Grade 5 Below-Level Collection)
ISBN 10: 0-15-357571-9 (package of 5)
ISBN 13: 978-0-15-357571-6 (package of 5)

2 3 4 5 6 7 8 9 10   126   12 11 10 09 08 07

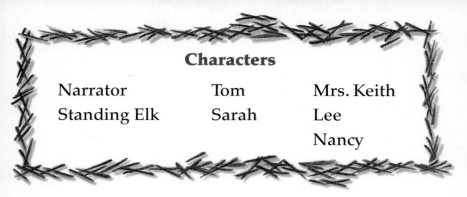

Characters

Narrator	Tom	Mrs. Keith
Standing Elk	Sarah	Lee
		Nancy

Narrator: Mrs. Keith and her students are exploring Redwood National Park with their guide, Standing Elk.

Standing Elk: Welcome to Redwood National Park! My name is Standing Elk. I'll be your guide today. My people have lived on this land for many years. This park has many kinds of trees, but it is named for an exceptional one: the redwood tree. You can see what a regal tree it is. Our walk won't be too grueling. The terrain here is rather even.

Tom: Wow! I'm not accustomed to seeing trees this big! I can't see the tops of the trees even if I squint!

Sarah: How tall are these trees?

Standing Elk: These trees here are not even the tallest redwoods in the park. These are about 200 feet (61.0 m) tall.

Mrs. Keith: How tall is the tallest redwood in Redwood National Park?

Standing Elk: The tallest redwood ever measured here was 367.8 feet (112.1 m) tall. That's equivalent to a little more than sixty-one refrigerators stacked one on top of the other.

Lee: That's amazing! How long does it take to grow that tall?

Standing Elk: It takes about 600 years. These trees can live for 2,000 years. Redwoods used to grow everywhere around here. Then settlers began moving to the West. They started cutting down the trees. Within less than a hundred years, only a small area was left. The redwood forests were in grave peril.

Mrs. Keith: I am appalled that people would do such a thing.

Standing Elk: Many people were upset. They started buying land here so that they could protect the redwoods. They believed that it was essential to protect this forest.

Sarah: It's so quiet here! The tranquility is stunning. Do animals live in this forest?

Tom: Don't be silly! Of course there are animals in this forest.

Sarah: I'm not silly! I was asking a question.

Mrs. Keith: Stop bickering. Apologize for being rude, Tom. Let Standing Elk answer the question.

Tom: I'm sorry, Sarah. However, I am sure that Standing Elk will say that there are plenty of animals that live in this forest.

Standing Elk: Yes, Tom, you're right. Let's keep walking, and I'll tell you more about this forest. We have many kinds of animals here. We have bats and foxes. We have wrens and jays, chickadees and owls. We have frogs and, of course, many kinds of insects. Stand still for a minute and be quiet. I'll poke under this leaf litter, and we'll see what is living right beneath our feet.

Sarah: There are lots of insects living in those dead leaves.

Standing Elk: Do you know why these insects are important?

Nancy: We studied this in class. Insects help get rid of the dead plants and animals. They help enrich the soil with nutrients so plants can grow.

Lee: Is that a salamander?

Standing Elk: Yes, you're right. It's a California slender salamander.

Mrs. Keith: We have been studying endangered animals in class. Are there any endangered animals here in the park?

Standing Elk: Yes, we have several animals here that need to be protected because their numbers are insufficient. Some are threatened with extinction. Others are in even more danger and are on the endangered list. The bald eagle is an endangered animal. It has come back in other parts of the United States. Here in California, though, it's still on our endangered animal list.

Tom: Will we see a bald eagle today? That would be so cool!

Standing Elk: If we're very lucky, we might see one later on, hunting for its food.

Sarah: However, eagles don't live in the forest, do they? I thought they always lived near water.

Nancy: I thought they needed room to soar around in the sky. You can hardly see the sky here.

Standing Elk: You're both right. Eagles make their nests in high perches so that they can look for snakes, mice, fish, and other animals to eat. You won't see eagles on this part of the trail, but gold miners once used this trail.

Lee: People searched for gold in this park?

Standing Elk: Yes, for a while, in the 1800s, it was customary to see miners here among the redwoods.

Lee: Are there any dangerous animals in the park?

Standing Elk: Just about any animal can be dangerous if you provoke it. It's always wise to keep your distance from animals in the park. We do have gray foxes, black bears, and bobcats in the forest part of the park. The black bears are potentially the most dangerous. Can anyone guess why?

Nancy: Black bears are probably the most dangerous because they are huge.

Standing Elk: That's right! In this part of the park, black bears are the biggest animals you will see. There are some other large animals in the ocean and prairie parts of the park.

Tom: I thought this park was just about the redwood trees.

Standing Elk: No, the redwood forest is only one habitat here. Another habitat is covered with grass. It's our prairie. There you can see black bears as well as another very large animal. Can you guess what that animal is? I'll give you a hint. I was named for this animal.

Lee: It's the elk!

Standing Elk: You kids are so smart! Your intelligence will undoubtedly lead to many great achievements.

Nancy: Standing Elk, where did all the redwoods go? These trees look like the spruce trees we have back home.

Standing Elk: You are right again, Nancy. These are spruce trees. Now take a deep breath, and tell me what you smell.

Lee, Tom, Sarah, and Nancy: It's the ocean!

Mrs. Keith: Does that mean that redwood trees do not like the salt air by the ocean? That's why they do not grow here? Spruce trees grow here instead?

Standing Elk: You kids have a very smart teacher! The kind of spruce trees we have here are called Sitka spruce. These are strong plants. They like ocean breezes and fog. They can live poised on the steep slopes near the ocean. Redwoods can't live too close to the ocean because of its salt winds and harsh conditions. Having the spruce trees here helps protect them.

Sarah: Look, everyone! That's a whale!

Tom: I think I see some dolphins, too!

Lee: This is just fantastic!

Mrs. Keith: Look over on those isolated rocks. I think those are harbor seals. We saw those at the aquarium. Do you remember how earnestly they swam around and around their tank?

Lee: I think they thought we had fish to feed them!

Standing Elk: We'll walk down along the beach. The tide is out. The rocks trap water in small pools. You might find some starfish and crabs and other interesting animals there. We'll head back in a little while. What's your favorite part of the tour so far?

Tom: I liked seeing the whales!

Nancy: I couldn't believe the size of the redwoods!

Lee: I liked spotting that salamander!

Sarah: Yuck! I didn't like that part. I did like watching the dolphins jump and play, though.

Mrs. Keith: It sounds like Redwood National Park has something for everyone to love!

Everyone: It sure does!